AMATEUR RADIO FOR BEGINNERS

HOW TO DISCOVER THE HOBBY

Victor Brand, G3JNB

Radio Society of Great Britain

Published by the Radio Society of Great Britain, Cranborne Road, Potters Bar, Herts
EN6 3JE

First published 1991

ISBN 1 872309 06 2

Design and typography by Ray Eckersley, Seven Stars Publishing, Marlow.
Printed in Great Britain by The Bath Press, Lower Bristol Road, Bath BA2 3BL.

Contents

Preface

Amateur radio is truly a hobby of the Space Age. Over one and a half million people of all ages are 'on the air' from their own homes, clubs and schools throughout the world.

Amateur Radio for Beginners is a simple introduction to this exciting hobby, and is written specifically for the absolute beginner. It will show you how to tune into the fascinating world of short-wave radio, how to make a crystal set, and just how to go about becoming a radio amateur.

Victor Brand, G3JNB
Norfolk, 1991

Acknowledgements

The author wishes to express his thanks for the generous support and assistance given by the Radio Society of Great Britain in the preparation of this book, especially to John Case, GW4HWR, for his work in preparing the practical materials and text for the crystal set, and also to Hilary Claytonsmith, G4JKS, and David Evans, G3OUF, for reviewing the manuscript.

CHAPTER 1

Amateur radio... today

"Hello Space Shuttle... this is radio station GB3RS at RSGB Headquarters. Do you read me?"

"GB3RS... this is W0ORE on board the US Space Shuttle. You are loud and clear!"

A MATEUR RADIO or, as some people call it, 'ham' radio, is now a regular feature of life in space. Using their personal radio 'callsigns', orbiting American and Russian astronauts are talking back to their friends on earth, using VHF radio on the wavebands that are used by amateurs.

All over the world, young people are joining in the fun, communicating with their real-life, space-age heroes from amateur radio stations at home, schools and universities.

More experienced radio enthusiasts are 'working' each other through special satellites, built by leading amateur groups, which circle high above the earth.

Similarly, and yet unaided by satellites, hundreds of thousands of people are talking to each other directly over the air 24 hours a day, by bouncing radio waves off layers in the Earth's atmosphere.

Using simple home-made receivers and low-power transmitters, or the most advanced, ready-built sets, they may be operating their radio station from

The Space Shuttle lifting off from Cape Kennedy

This TV picture was sent to RSGB Headquarters by astronaut Tony England, who has the amateur radio callsign W0ORE, while he was on board the Space Shuttle

their 'radio shack' in a back bedroom, a garden shed or their local amateur radio club.

With a simple transmitting aerial in the garden, enthusiastic amateurs make the airwaves buzz with the excitement of making new radio contacts. Many stations keep regular appointments with friends all over the world.

Imagine the thrill of sitting in your own home and talking to South America or Australia. Or hearing a voice calling you from a remote Pacific island, or perhaps contacting a ship's radio officer who uses his own amateur callsign to operate in his off-duty hours. As the rest of the world listens, you chat away using your microphone, or perhaps 'speak' to each other in morse code that you tap out using a morse key connected to your transmitter.

If you have a computer, then you might handle the whole contact through your keyboard and screen, again connected to the transmitter, to flash your message across the oceans.

This exciting hobby enables you to make new friends and discover a whole new world. You can talk to other amateurs in the next road, in the next town or thousands of miles away! You learn about simple electronics in a way that is fun, while broadening your horizons.

Amateur Radio for Beginners will tell you how to discover the hobby of amateur radio for yourself. It will tell you just a little of what it is all about and could set you on a course for a lifetime of pleasure and personal satisfaction. The experience can certainly improve your general education, and possibly your career prospects. It will provide hours of pleasure and it can lead you into a wide circle of international friendships.

Talking on the air is a great way of making new friends of all ages. Here a Scout is operating station GB2GP at the Gilwell Park camp site near London   PHOTO: SCOUT ASSOCIATION

You can use your home computer to make contacts, too. This is G3UJV operating during the National Field Day contest

CHAPTER 2

You meet such interesting people

M OST people know very little about amateur radio. They may have a friend or relative who "talks to people on a radio set" or have seen stories in the newspapers about local amateurs providing emergency communications in times of crisis.

Unlike some pastimes, this hobby knows no boundaries. It is open to people in all walks of life, and kings and teenagers communicate on the air on equal terms.

His Majesty King Hussein operates his personal amateur radio station from the Royal Palace in Jordan using his amateur callsign JY1. King Juan Carlos of Spain and the former Prime Minister of India, Mr Rajiv Gandhi, are also licensed amateurs of long standing, as is Senator Barry Goldwater of the USA. Actors Sir Brian Rix and Marlon Brando, singer Ferghal Sharkey, guitarist Chet Atkins and broadcaster Chris Tarrant all hold amateur radio licences and have

Anglia TV weatherman Jim Bacon is a keen radio amateur, here operating a station at the White Rose amateur radio club in Leeds

The famous inventor Marconi demonstrating radio to the armed services and govern-ment officials on Salisbury Plain on 2 September 1896. Marconi subsequently became a member of the Radio Society of Great Britain   PAINTING: STEPHEN SPURRIER, ARA

been heard joining in the fun on the amateur bands. Informality prevails and you may never know who it is you are speaking to. You might chat away happily to a rare station in, say, South Africa without ever realising that your contact is with a bishop!

The first real radio amateur was the young Marconi. He was a founding father of radio broadcasting and the first person to establish wireless communication across the Atlantic in 1901. In those pioneering days, there were many young amateurs who pushed forward the frontiers of the science, using equipment they had to build entirely with their own hands – there were no handy radio shops or convenient mail-order suppliers.

Our grandfathers crouched over home-made crystal sets and listened hopefully on their headphones for the weak sound of station 2LO transmitting from London. To hear anything at all from this early broadcasting station was a thrill beyond description. How different to today's scene, with television and radio stations pouring out news, music and entertainment from all corners of the world. Now we take it for granted. Or do we?

Most Governments recognise the freedom of the air for suitably qualified citizens and support the view that amateur radio spreads international goodwill. The hobby provides a valuable means of self-education in electronics, geography and languages, as well as all manner of technical and mechanical skills. These are invaluable advantages indeed to people trying to keep up with today's rapidly advancing technology.

HRH Prince Phillip, Duke of Edinburgh, replying to a greetings message on the air at the Radio Society of Great Britain's 75th anniversary celebrations

In America, the State of New York has launched a new initiative by introducing amateur radio into the school curriculum in order to teach pupils simple electronics at an early age.

In 1989, Russian cosmonauts were taught the basics of amateur radio during their long stay in an orbiting space station and were issued with their callsigns there and then. They were subsequently heard all over the world by the listening enthusiasts and eagerly 'worked' by the lucky few.

Here in the UK in the same year, His Royal Highness Prince Philip, the Duke of Edinburgh, as Patron of the Radio Society of Great Britain, announced the beginning of Project YEAR – 'Youth into Electronics via Amateur Radio'. The purpose of the Project is to smooth the way for beginners aspiring to an amateur licence, to encourage people to study electronics as a hobby and to help equip them for a future in communication technology.

Through the Radiocommunications Agency (RA) of the Department of Trade and Industry, the British Government has publicly stated its active support for amateur radio as a vital link in the education of the next generation of electronic experts. It is keen to see that Great Britain continues to maintain its historic position as one of the world's leading pioneers in all things electronic, including satellite communications and computer technology.

To emphasise the importance of Project Year to the nation, the RA has also initiated an annual award to the 'Young Amateur of the Year'. In 1988 the first such award was made to schoolboy Andrew Keeble, then aged 15, for his outstanding progress as a radio amateur and his work in the community. Using his own station callsign G1XYE, Andrew participated in amateur radio emergency services in his home town of Norwich, and actively used his radio skills to promote his other

Young Amateurs of the Year. Top: Andrew Keeble, G1XYE (1988). Lower left: Ted Walker, G0KAQ (1989). Lower right: David Martin, GM0NVE (1990)

Amateur radio rallies are held throughout the year where you can find great bargains and meet your friends. This one was at the G-Mex Centre in Manchester

interests in Scouting and membership of the St John Ambulance Brigade. Not surprisingly, his success increased his popularity in amateur circles and also resulted in invitations that are expected to lead to an exciting career in electronics.

Meeting people is important to us all, both socially and from the point of view of experience. Although our hobby may keep us comfortably at home for much of the time, operating our station or building a new radio, the opportunity to become a member of a local radio club is open to all, beginners and experts alike.

It is in the company of the more experienced that the beginner can enjoy the true fellowship of the world of amateur radio. A few words with the right club members and all sorts of help is usually forthcoming. They all remember the time when they, too, were getting started and did not know one

end of a transistor from another. Licensed amateurs and listeners alike enjoy demonstrations and talks by leading amateurs, equipment sales and field events.

Many clubs run classes to teach people the basics of radio in order to qualify for an amateur licence. They also teach members morse code and the correct procedures for operating a station on the air.

Throughout the year, rallies and exhibitions are mounted nationwide at which new and second-hand equipment, simple kits, components and books are sold, and at which talks and demonstrations take place. National events frequently attract thousands of amateurs, whilst the smaller local shows are supported by a few hundred, among whom will be people you may have spoken to regularly over the air but previously have never met face-to-face.

Amateur radio is full of surprises. For

The author received this QSL card from Eric, VK7AAB, as a confirmation of the contact; it shows a photo of Swan Island

instance, you just do not know who you may contact next. During the writing of this chapter, the author was in touch regularly with an Australian amateur station, Eric, VK7AAB, located on the tiny Swan Island just off the north eastern tip of Tasmania. In a series of hour-long contacts each morning, we talked of life on his island and its fascinating history.

According to Eric, it was used as a settlement for the original Tasmanian Aborigines by the Europeans who wanted them off the mainland. In later years, a lighthouse was built and three houses were constructed for the keepers. Today, Swan Island remains an important light for shipping, although it is now totally automated and powered by a wind generator.

Ex-airline pilot Eric and his wife Mary decided to retire to the wonderful peace and quiet. He acts as the local 'weather man' and provides the authorities with regular bulletins. A small airplane is their only means of crossing to the mainland and Swan Island depends entirely on radio for communication. The telephone is linked by microwave across the water to the local exchange; Citizen's Band

A map of Tasmania showing Swan Island. Why not try to find it in your atlas?

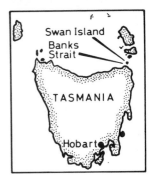

radio is the means of ordering groceries from the supermarket; and, of course, amateur radio brings the world right into their home, giving them the means to stay constantly in touch with many friends.

Such contacts really do demonstrate both the fun and the educational value of becoming an amateur. Would you have known where Swan Island was located or have had any idea of its history?

For the beginner, the hobby may seem rather 'technical' but, once you get started, all will become clear.

CHAPTER 3

How to get started

T RADITIONALLY, a radio amateur starts out in the hobby by just listening to the signals on the amateur short-wave bands. In this way, the beginner gets the feel of what it is all about and learns how amateurs communicate. At the same time, the conversations coming in over the air can teach the listener a good deal about basic radio theory.

Many enthusiasts choose to remain as short-wave listeners throughout their lives, developing quite remarkable skills in the reception of the many unusual stations that appear on the air from all over the world. They monitor signals from experimental stations, listen to expeditions to the North and South Poles or to remote and uninhabited islands. They write the details of all they hear in their station log and may later confirm in writing that they have heard the expedition operators. In return, they hope to receive confirmation of their reports in the form of a 'QSL card'.

Similarly, many people also listen to the international short-wave broadcasting stations that transmit programmes in English and various other languages. It is interesting to listen to a direct, short-wave broadcast from a world event such as the Olympic Games on your own

Listening to the signals on the amateur short-wave bands is an ideal start to the hobby

The shack of an established listener. These can rival those of transmitting amateurs

home-made radio and then to tune to the amateur bands and hear the amateurs of the same nation discussing the day's events with friends across the world.

The first principle of amateur radio is to learn how to listen. Before any contact can be made with that exotic station in the far-off East Indies, you must be able to hear him! Simply learn to listen, because to listen is to learn. Once you have mastered the art of tuning in to the amateur bands and are able to follow all that is going on, it is time to think about getting your own transmitting licence.

The Novice Licence is an ideal first stepping stone. Here in the UK this is issued by the Radiocommunications Agency. Every licence is given a unique callsign so the user can be identified on the air.

Every radio station in the world has to respect international regulations to safeguard the airwaves from poorly adjusted transmitters, and to avoid

signals interfering with each other. Since most people who take up the hobby have little or no technical knowledge or experience, the licensing authorities of every nation insist that the applicant first proves he or she is competent by passing a standard test in amateur radio theory and practice.

Written tests are held by the City and Guilds Institute in various centres each year and the pass rate is generally good. A pass in these fairly straightforward multiple-choice examinations qualifies the applicant to hold a Novice Class B amateur licence with a personal callsign, and gives permission for speech transmitting equipment to be installed and used on some sections of the VHF (very high frequency) amateur bands.

The passing of a test in morse, at a relatively slow speed of five words a minute, qualifies you for a Novice Class A licence, a new callsign and access to certain portions of the world-wide HF (high frequency) amateur bands.

Worksheets

First soldering exercise

TEST SET No. 1

The first objective in this exercise – to practice soldering and to make a basic TEST SET. You will use this later for a number of different tests.

Check your materials – A piece of wood or chipboard bigger than the outline in the diagram which has been drawn actual size to make it easier to get the parts in the right places. A bulbholder, a 2.5 Volt, 0.2 Amp bulb, two battery boxes for AA size cells, an 8.2 Ohm, 0.25 Watt resistor (Grey, red, gold), a 2.2 Ohm, 0.25 Watt resistor (Red, red, gold), seven brass drawing pins and about 300mm of tinned copper wire. You will also need a soldering iron, an iron stand, some resin cored solder, a pair of wire cutters and a pair of 'long nosed' pliers.

CONSTRUCTION.

Look at the diagram and compare it with the parts.

The bulbholder and the battery boxes may be in position already. If they are not, mount them in the positions shown with very small screws or pieces of 'blu tac'. Fix two solder tags under the terminal screws of the bulbholder. Push the seven drawing pins into the positions shown – try to be as accurate as possible but do not push them down to the board at this stage!

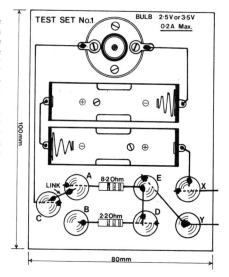

Carefully solder pieces of wire and the two resistors to complete the circuit exactly as shown in the diagram but first READ ON.

A page from the *Student's Notebook* for the Novice Licence

Building simple radios is fun

The Radio Society of Great Britain holds morse tests regularly in all parts of the country for anybody wishing to qualify.

Rest assured that the learning of a little theory and becoming familiar with the regulations is well worth the effort. It equips you with sufficient knowledge to enjoy your amateur activities to the full. It also gives you the opportunity to experiment, to build and operate radio equipment with far greater freedom than that permitted to the professional broadcasting stations that are so closely supervised.

Don't be concerned about your abilities to learn enough to pass the tests. People of all ages and backgrounds qualify for the licences every year, many of whom had absolutely no prior technical knowledge. They find amateur radio a new and absorbing outlet for their energies and a fascinating hobby for their leisure hours.

There is a wide variety of popular books that can help you to acquire your new knowledge. Beginners' courses are available at local level which are organised by the Radio Society of Great Britain (see chapter 12). The technical side is not very difficult, especially if you have studied elementary physics at school. In any case, once you get involved you will find that it is easier to pick up the theory and jargon of amateur radio than it is to get started in many hobbies or sports.

There is no substitute for the thrill of making a simple radio set that works well enough to bring in signals from, say, local broadcasting stations. The building of one's first receiver is an unforgettable experience and hearing your first signals on it is an important point from which most of us start on a lifetime as amateur radio communicators.

No transistor radio or mighty 'ghettoblaster', however blessed with hi-tech features, can provide the satisfaction or

An advanced type of communication receiver

PHOTO: SOUTH MIDLANDS COMMUNICATIONS

the sense of accomplishment that is felt when first you switch on your home-made receiver and hear a station on your headphones or loudspeaker.

In spite of supermarkets stacked with attractively packaged produce, home-made jam and home-made bread are still reckoned to be the most appetising. So it is with our hobby. There is far more satisfaction in making your own radio. Furthermore, home-made equipment accounts for many new developments or 'breakthroughs' in modern technology that originate from the amateur movement.

There is a variety of ready-built short-wave radio receivers for those who wish to progress rather more quickly, or who perhaps have already enjoyed the fun of a home construction set. However, it is important to understand that in many cases the modern 'all-waveband' transistor radios are not suitable for listening to amateurs.

Of course, to listen to the broadcasting stations of the world they can be excellent, but to tune into the amateur frequencies they must be equipped with a switch or control, usually marked 'BFO' or 'Beat Frequency Oscillator', to help resolve the types of signals that are now transmitted by amateur stations. The use of this control is explained later.

To have the capacity to hear the world's amateurs really well and to enjoy the hobby to the full, a more advanced type of 'communication receiver' is required. It may be a set designed to receive amateur signals on just one band or a set that switches from one amateur band to another and which can resolve speech or morse with ease.

Listening will provide an extraordinary insight into the world of amateur radio and international broadcasting. The pleasurable hours spent at the receiver are all part of the important 'learning curve' that you will follow in your quest for knowledge and experience.

The whole world of short-wave radio is one of excitement. In this almost magical form of communication, your voice is travelling around the world at an amazing 186,500 miles per second! The study of how radio signals travel or 'propagate' as if by magic is fascinating and yet is easily accessible to us all.

Remember, learn first to listen. As the old amateur saying goes, "if you cannot hear them you cannot work them".

CHAPTER 4

How to make your first receiver

IN the early days of radio, the most popular receiver was the crystal set. It needed no battery and used few components. Millions of people all over the world made their own sets and connected up a pair of headphones, rather like those of the modern personal stereos, plugged in an aerial wire leading in from the garden and sat entranced by the faint sounds of music that came over the air.

To gain a little practical experience, and before you venture onto the short-wave bands with something a little more advanced, why not make yourself a modern-day version of the crystal set? For an hour or two of your time and a very modest cost, you can build a set that, at the very least, should receive a local broadcasting station on medium wave. (Note: if you do not have a local station with a strong signal, this design may not work too well.)

No technical knowledge is necessary and the bits and pieces required are readily obtainable from your local radio component shop or by mail order.

So, how do you make a start? To 'tune-in' a signal, you require a coil of wire and a component called a variable capacitor, which simply consists of two sets of thin metal plates that can be intermeshed with one another by turning a spindle or screw. As you will see later, the coil and the capacitor are wired together to form an electrical 'circuit' that will tune into the 'frequency' of the station you require.

In order to hear, or 'detect' the signals, a 'diode' is connected to the tuning circuit together with a 'high-impedance' *crystal* earpiece. (Hi-fi or personal stereo headphones will not work well in this circuit.)

To pick up the medium wave programmes from your local BBC or commercial station (this set is not suitable for the VHF/FM services), you will need a long aerial wire, preferably high up in the open air, connected to one end of your coil and, for best results, an earth wire clipped onto the other. This earth wire is simply connected to your cold water pipe (assuming it is metal) or run out to a metal rod that should be driven into the earth just outside your window.

Remember, a crystal set has no internal battery power source of its own. Believe it or not, the electrical currents that 'circulate' through the components and drive the headphones come over the air from the transmitter of the broadcasting station. Of course this free 'power' is very, very small by the time it arrives at your home and, normally, would be amplified in your radio to provide a good volume of sound from its loudspeaker.

Nevertheless, the tiny radio frequency signals are there and need to be 'picked up' or collected by using an aerial and earth of a size that will deliver sufficient energy to make your circuit work. Obviously there will be differences in the amount of energy available at your location according to how far you live from the broadcasting transmitter and just how long and how high you can place your aerial wire.

The components you will need

To simplify construction and experimentation, no soldering is required. All you will need are a small screwdriver, some wire cutters and something with which to make suitable holes. Some connections are made by fitting miniature crocodile clips to the leads and the use of a terminal block, methods that allow for quick assembly and easy adjustment. Step-by-step instructions for assembly are given later.

The coil

You will need some thin insulated copper wire for the coil. By 'thin', I mean that the copper part of it inside the insulation should only measure less than 1 millimetre in diameter. If you are ordering it from a radio shop, specify 28 SWG (Standard Wire Gauge), which is 0.4mm diameter. It should be insulated with an enamel covering.

The coil

The coil is formed by winding a number of turns onto a cylindrical tube – a cardboard tube from a toilet-roll is ideal. Note that metal tubes are not suitable. This tube is known as the 'former'.

The number of wire turns will depend on the diameter of your tube and the electrical value of your capacitor. With a toilet-roll tube you will need 80 turns. Varying the number of turns can be a

useful experiment to check for best performance.

The variable capacitor

Variable capacitors come in a variety of shapes, sizes and values. The size is not important as long as you can fit it onto the baseboard.

Just as petrol comes in litres and sugar in kilos, the value of a capacitor is measured in units known as 'farads', or small parts of a farad known as 'picofarads'. When you are asking for the capacitor for the receiver, specify a 100-500 picofarad compression trimmer type.

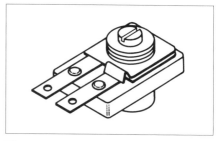

The compression trimmer

The 'proper' variable capacitors, as used in commercial radios, are rather expensive, costing £5 or more, so the cheaper compression trimmer capacitor can be used in the design that follows. This has a screw as a tuning control, rather than a metal shaft, and therefore cannot be fitted with a tuning knob. However, if you can afford a 'proper' capacitor, or you can borrow one from a radio amateur, the following notes may help.

If you are asked if you want an air-spaced or solid-dielectric version, take whichever you can afford or can see is easiest to fix, for in this case it doesn't really matter which you use.

When you examine the capacitor, you will see that there are several connection tags, or 'terminals'. Some will be connected to the moving plates of metal and the others to the fixed ones. The spindle enables you to turn the moving plates in and out of the fixed plates and vary the value of the capacitor, thus tuning the coil circuit to find the station. Most variable capacitors will also have a nut round the neck of the spindle to allow you to fix the components through a hole in the front panel of the radio. If yours has no such mounting then you will have to come up with a means of holding it in place without hindering the tuning action.

With a proper variable capacitor, a knob can be slipped onto the spindle to allow you to turn the plates comfortably without touching the metal with your hands – which can upset the tuning. Some of these knobs are simply fixed by being pushed on, while others have a small 'grub' screw in the side, which is tightened to hold the knob in place. Be warned, these tiny screws are very difficult to find if you drop them on the carpet!

The fixed capacitors
These are similar to the variable capacitor described above, except that they have a fixed value. In this circuit, both are 100 picofarads capacitors.

The fixed capacitor

The diode
Early crystal sets depended on a 'detector' that was very tricky to adjust. A small piece of crystalline mineral – hence the name 'crystal set' – was placed in a holder and tickled with a very fine piece of springy wire. This 'cat's whisker' seemed to have a life of its own. Sometimes it found a good spot on the crystal and provided superb detection, and other times it simply did not work. Listeners would spend hours adjusting their detectors for the best signal.

The diode

Detection can now be accomplished easily by using a tiny diode that will work without human aid! There are all sorts of diodes. They are cheap and come with wire ends, ready for you to fit to your terminal strip. If you go to buy one, ask for a diode suitable for a crystal set, such as an AA119, OA47, OA71 or OA91.

The resistor
This small component 'resists' the passage of electricity through it, hence its name. Electrical resistance is measured in 'ohms', named after another famous scientist, Georg Ohm, and in this circuit, the resistor has a value of 100,000 ohms (100 kilo-ohms or 100k for short).

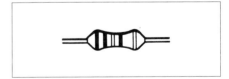

The resistor. In this circuit the first three coloured bands should be (left to right) brown, black and yellow

The earpiece
An earpiece (or headphones) are just the thing to listen to weak signals. Unlike a loudspeaker, they require very little energy or power to produce a

sound in your ears. For use with this crystal set, it must have a high 'impedance' and therefore 'crystal' types are the most likely to be available, although high-impedance magnetic headphones may sometimes be found in junk shops or at amateur radio rallies. Hi-fi or personal stereo headphones are not suitable.

Earpieces and headphones come with a plug on the end called a 'jack plug'. Two types of plug are common – the quarter-inch diameter type used for ordinary headphones, or the miniature 3.5mm diameter type used with earpieces and personal stereos. You will also need a matching jack socket to include in your circuit so that you can simply plug in your earpiece. So just ask for a 3.5mm or a quarter-inch jack socket, depending upon the type of headphone plug you have.

The circuit

It would be very difficult for designers of radio and TV sets if they had to show pictures of all the components when designing the circuit of a new model. Instead, they use symbols as a type of shorthand for every different component, which are recognised internationally.

The symbols that interest you are these:

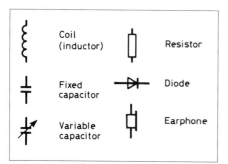

Taking these symbols – here is your crystal set circuit. It shows the components and the wiring connections that

will make the circuit come to life when you clip on the aerial and earth.

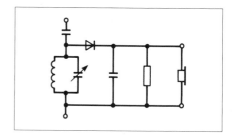

There are also symbols for an aerial and earth. These are:

So, by adding these to the original you end up with this circuit diagram, which all experienced amateurs will recognise immediately as a basic crystal set receiver.

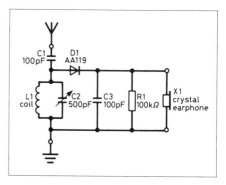

Buying the parts

The components should be easily obtainable at a low cost from any amateur radio shop. Your local radio and television servicing centre may be able to help you or you can order through the mail from Cirkit or Maplin. The high street Tandy stores usually

CRYSTAL SET COMPONENTS LIST

One four-way 2A terminal block (12-way divided into three)
One 100-500pF compression trimmer
One diode, type AA119. (Other types suitable are: OA47, OA90, OA91, or OA95)
One 100k, 0.6 watt resistor
Two 100pF capacitors
One PCB miniature jack socket
One crystal earpiece

The cost of the above components is about £2.50 in 1991.

Also required:
5 metres of 0.375 or 0.4mm (28 SWG) enamel-covered wire
A few pieces of PVC-covered wire
A small bracket for the jack socket
A wooden block
Two drawing pins
Two thin buttons (shirt)
Four small screws or nails (10/12mm)
Sticky pads or Blu-Tack
Four miniature crocodile clips

have a supply of good-quality components.

Seek the advice of an assistant with some knowledge of amateur radio and be prepared to accept equivalent or near-equivalent components as the values are not critical.

A shopping list, with a rough indication of the cost at the time of going to press, appears on this page.

Building the set

Take a close look at the photograph and you will see how the components are built onto the baseboard. To wire up your circuit using the clips and odd pieces of wire, follow these 10 easy steps.

1. Making the baseboard

Almost any piece of soft wood at least as big as the full-size drawing shown over the page will do. Sandpaper and paint the board with any household paint left over from the last decorating job. Leave to dry, and while you are waiting you could carry on with step 2.

When the board is dry, trace the outline and crosses in the diagram onto paper, then transfer to the top surface of your board. This can be done quite simply by pricking the corners and the crosses with the point of a pair of compasses or something similar.

Drill a hole at 'A' using a 4mm drill. The hole should be at least as deep as

The completed set

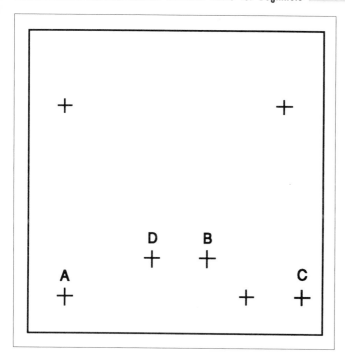

Making the base-board, which is shown here full-size

the length of the thread on the back of the trimmer capacitor. Try to find someone who has a drill of the correct size and get them to drill the hole. If this is not possible, make a fairly deep hole with the point of the compasses and enlarge it with a small screwdriver, then follow with a larger one.

Prick fairly deep holes at positions 'B' and 'C'.

2. Constructing the coil

This should be wound as described earlier, using 0.4mm enamel-covered wire. The former is the cardboard tube from a toilet roll. Choose one which is not falling to pieces and has a diameter of about 40mm. Make two holes 20mm from one end for the start of the winding. Thread the wire through these holes, leaving at least 100mm free, and then wind on 80 turns. These should be an even layer with the turns touching but not on top of one another – take your

time. Finish with two more holes, again leaving a 'tail' of 100mm. If you have wound your coil carefully and with the correct size wire, the length of the winding should be about 30 to 32mm. Give both coil and tube a coat of clear varnish. Leave to dry for at least 24 hours, then carefully cut the tube so that it is 70mm long, with the coil in the centre.

3. Examining the terminal block

Look at it carefully. Inside the plastic there are four metal tubes with a terminal screw at each end. In the drawing these tubes are labelled '1', '2', '3', and '4'. It makes no difference if a connection is made at one end or the other but having two ends makes it easier to arrange the wires and components.

4. Marking the base again

Place the terminal block on your base

26

board with the terminal screws facing up. Move it about until you can see the hole you pricked at 'B' through the right-hand fixing hole of the block. Press one of the nails into the hole and push it down gently. Move the block again and you should be able to see the cross marked 'D' in the left-hand fixing hole of the block. Get it to the centre of the hole or as near as you can, then put the second nail into the left-hand hole and press. Remove the block; the dent made by the second nail should be very close to the cross marked 'D'. Prick this dent fairly hard, again using the compass point.

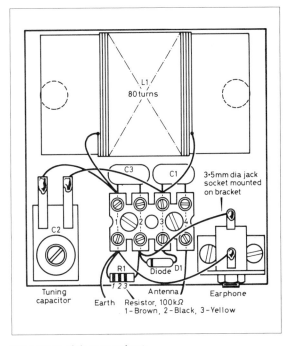

The layout of the crystal set

5. Preparing the terminal block

Take great care with this step. Spread out a sheet of newspaper or something to catch a screw if it should fall. Hold the terminal block so that you are looking into the tubes and with a thin screwdriver carefully unscrew the terminal's screws so you can see through the tubes. You may have to buy a suitable screwdriver (called a 'terminal screwdriver') but don't worry – they only cost about 20p. Do this with all eight terminals. Don't unscrew too far as the screws may fall out and they can be very difficult to find – especially in a carpet.

6. Fitting the components

Keep referring to the diagram above showing the overall layout. Start with the two capacitors; they are the same so it doesn't matter which you use first – look at the diagram.

The capacitors C1 and C3. Pass the two leads of C3 through tubes 1 and 2,

press the component gently up to the plastic. Both leads will stick out on the opposite side of the block. Mark one lead where it comes out of the block. See the arrow in the diagram over the page showing the connector block. A felt-tip pen will be useful for marking the wire. Remove the capacitor, and cut the lead at the mark using wire cutters or an *old* pair of scissors. Put the capacitor back into the block but this time don't push it up to the plastic. Tighten the screw nearest to the capacitor in tube 2. Note: the other lead of the capacitor must not be cut as it will form the earth terminal. Repeat the process with C1 and fit it to tubes 3 and 4. The long lead should come out of terminal 4 and will be the aerial terminal.

The resistor is fitted to tubes 1 and 2. In this case, both wires should be cut to 20mm, bent at right angles to the body of the resistor.

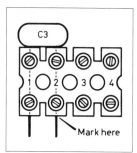

The connector block

Remove about 5mm of the plastic covering from one end of a 60mm length of wire and insert the end into tube 2 with the resistor. Tighten the terminal screw at the resistor end of tube 1.

The diode is a small glass tube which must not be confused with the resistor.

Cut the leads to 20mm – take great care not to disturb the delicate junction inside. Hold the wire in the jaws of a pair of pliers and cut the wire on the side away from the diode. Fit the diode to terminals 2 and 3. Tighten terminal 3 (nearest to the diode).

Remove 5mm of insulation from another piece of wire, also 60mm long. Fit the bare wire to terminal 2 and tighten the screw. All screws on the side of the block against the diode and resistor should now be tight.

Terminals 1 and 3 on the other side should *not* be tightened yet.

7. Fitting the tuning capacitor

Remove the nut and washer from the back of the 'trimmer' capacitor. If you managed to get the hole drilled to the correct size you will find that the capacitor will screw into hole A. If the hole was made by 'other' means, the capacitor will probably not screw in. In this case make the hole big enough to allow the capacitor to 'sit' on the board and use a dab of glue to fix it. Don't use too much or the capacitor will fail to work correctly.

If you can solder, fit two leads to the terminals of the capacitor and connect

them to tubes 1 and 3 of the terminal block.

If not, connect the wires to the capacitor terminals using small crocodile clips. To connect the wire to the clip, just undo the little screw, thread the wire through the neck of the clip, wind in around the screw and tighten up.

8. Fitting the jack socket

Ideally, the jack socket should be mounted on a small aluminium bracket which is screwed to the baseboard as shown in the photo. The terminals of the jack must be facing up. If you don't have a bracket, then you will have to use sticky pads or Blu-Tack to fix the socket to the board.

Again, if you can solder, fix two pieces of wire to the two solder tags as shown in the second diagram. The jack socket will probably have three solder tags – if so, do not use the tag on the left-hand side. If you can't solder, use the above crocodile clip method to fix the wires to the socket.

Connect the two wires from the socket to terminals 1 and 2 on the terminal strip and tighten both screws.

9. Connecting the coil

Fix the coil near to the edge of the base board using two drawing pins so that the wires come out of the coil near to the terminal strip. Look at the layout diagram again. Cut the wires so that they will easily reach the terminal strip, then rub off the enamel insulation from the last 10mm using sandpaper, so the metal shines brightly. Clean the ends with a paper tissue.

Connect the wires to sockets 1 and 3 on the terminal strip and tighten the screws. Check that all eight terminal screws are tight. The receiver is complete.

10. The aerial and earth

Now you are nearly ready. Finally, however, there is the matter of the aerial

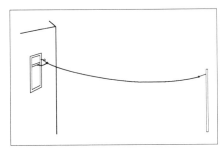

A small hook in the window frame can hold one end of your aerial and a post on the garden fence the other

and earth. Ideally, your aerial should be out of doors and as high as possible. Take a look at the picture and you will see the idea. Usually the length of aerial will determine the strength of the signal that a crystal set will receive. The more wire, the stronger the signal. With this simple circuit, however, the greater the length of wire the poorer the selectivity of your tuning – that is, the ability of the set to separate one station from another.

Your location will dictate the size of your aerial. About 50 feet of wire should be enough but be prepared to experiment with shorter or longer lengths.

To make a good earth, you will need to run a wire from your receiver to a copper or brass earthing rod that is then driven into the earth at the nearest point. Don't use an iron rod, as it will rust. Make sure both your wire and the rod are scraped clean before you connect them together with a nut and bolt. Wrap the joint with plastic insulating tape to protect it from corrosion. If you are in a flat or too far up from the garden, try clipping your earth to a radiator or to a metal water pipe, choosing a point where some bare metal is exposed.

Testing the set

Plug in the earpiece, connect the aerial to terminal 4 and the earth to terminal 1, again using a crocodile clip for the connections. Listen very carefully as you adjust the screw on the tuning capacitor. The signals are very weak so it is important to listen when there is no other noise.

If you hear nothing, count the number of wires going to each tube of the terminal block and compare with those shown in the layout diagram. Check that all other connections are correct. Look at the wires from the coil – make sure that the enamel has been cleaned off.

If you can hear one or two stations but the screw of the tuning capacitor is almost completely out, remove about five turns from the coil, being careful to ensure that the end of the wire is clean when you reconnect it to the block. If the stations are still only heard with the tuning capacitor screw very loose, remove a few more turns from the coil, but not more than 10 in total.

It works? Great! Your first home-made receiver and your very first signal is something that you will remember for the rest of your life!

To improve your set's performance, try different aerial lengths, reversing the diode and receiving with and without the earth connected. Do not expect to get the same reception and volume that your transistor set produces. However, the author's own set, built at the age of 15 inside a cardboard shoebox, provided hours of nightly listening in bed, at a strength that required the headphones to be hidden under the pillow to avoid attracting the attention of my parents! Incidentally, you will find that some signals tend to be louder after dark.

If you just cannot get your circuit to work, then you may have to get help from your local radio club, which you may already know or perhaps can contact by getting in touch with the Radio Society of Great Britain (see appendix).

This little crystal set should give you hours of fun whilst you progress to the next stage of the hobby... listening on short-wave and amateur bands.

CHAPTER 5

Learning the language of radio – 1

MANY people mistakenly think that radio and electronics are far too technical for them to understand. Perhaps they should appreciate that just as the term 'LBW' means a great deal to keen cricketers, or 'bain marie' is very clear to the cook, the names given to the various components and activities enjoyed by electronics enthusiasts are just as essential to their hobby.

Naturally, a radio amateur starts with the simple stuff – just like every other person taking up a new sport, hobby or pursuit. By taking things in easy stages you will soon find yourself speaking the language or jargon of the amateur. Indeed, have you noticed how much you know already? By just reading this book as far as this page and building the crystal set you will now be familiar with some of the most basic terms. What are they? Well, let's recap...

Aerial The wire that picks up or radiates (sends out) a radio signal. Sometimes called an *antenna*.

Amateur radio The hobby of radio communication, sometimes called *ham radio*.

BFO Beat frequency oscillator. A circuit that assists a receiver to read morse. Also necessary to resolve amateur *SSB* speech (see later).

Callsign The unique identifying numbers, letters or name given to every radio station under licence.

Capacitor Metal or foil plates that are insulated from one another. Comes in variable and fixed form and provides a required value of *capacitance* for a circuit.

Circuit diagram The design showing the layout of components and connections in a radio or other electronic equipment.

Coil Wire wound on a former, tuned with a capacitor to set a circuit to a required frequency.

Communication receiver An advanced radio set designed to receive weak signals, usually on short waves, and to hear types of transmission which you can't receive on an ordinary set.

Crocodile clip Handy clip for wire ends.

Crystal set Basic radio receiver.

Detector A device which resolves or *detects* radio signals carrying speech in an appropriate radio circuit.

Diode Can be used as a detector. It is a simple device that will conduct electrical current in only one direction.

Earth To increase aerial efficiency. Also required in an amateur station to 'ground' all equipment for safety.

A typical morse key

PHOTO: G4ZPY
PADDLE KEYS

Farad The basic measuring unit or value of a capacitor. Named after Michael Faraday, one of the pioneers of electrical theory.

Frequency The precise electronic measurement that determines where a station appears on your dial. Incidentally, the unit of frequency is the *hertz* – also named after an early pioneer, Heinrich Hertz. Thus, you will hear your local VHF/FM station say something like "98.4 megahertz" as the frequency of its transmission. Just in case you didn't know, *mega* means millions and *kilo* means thousands.

Grub-screw A headless securing screw.

Ham radio Traditional American term for amateur radio.

Headphones A headset that provides sound directly to the ears.

Homebrew Home-made.

Jack A plug usually used to connect two or three wires into circuit as required, via a *jack socket.*

Key A morse or telegraph key is used to send morse signals.

kHz Abbreviation of *kilohertz.*

Licence In this hobby, a licence is required before any station can transmit signals over the air.

Loudspeaker The component in a radio set or hi-fi system that vibrates the air to make the 'sound' that your ears can hear.

MHz Abbreviation of *megahertz.*

Morse code The dots and dashes that are sent with a key to form the words of messages.

Power Energy. Can be energy supplied by a battery or a power supply. Can be the energy in a circuit that produces a signal.

The author's radio shack

Radio shack The room in which a radio station is installed.

Receiver A radio set that receives signals from a transmitter.

Sked Broadcasting stations work to a schedule or set programme plan. Amateurs often arrange such a schedule, known as a 'sked', to meet another amateur on the air on a certain day, at a specified time and on a given frequency.

Short waves The 'long-distance' radio wavebands. Long and medium waves are the medium-distance broadcasting bands.

SWG Standard wire gauge – the size or thickness of wire, eg 20 SWG. The higher the number, the thinner the wire.

Terminals Means of electrical connection to a component by screw, clip or soldering.

Transmitter A radio that sends out signals by speech, morse or other types of communication.

VHF Very high frequency. Like *UHF* (ultra high frequency), VHF is the very-short-wave band used for more local signals like your local FM stations. Used extensively by amateurs for both local and specialised activities like satellite communications.

'Working' Jargon for communication with another radio station.

So, you see, it is not so difficult. By the time you have read the remaining chapters you will know even more and be ready to move on to learn from the books that are to follow in this series, and from the more advanced publications that are available from the Radio Society of Great Britain and other publishers.

CHAPTER 6

Listening on the short-wave bands

L ISTENING to broadcasting stations on short waves is a fascinating experience. Sounds from all over the world come pouring into your shack, with hot news, current affairs, live commentaries and ethnic music. They may originate from large studios in a major world capital, or from a modest station in a tiny far-off state which may have been unknown to you until you sat down in front of your receiver.

Such is the fine art of short-wave listening, and so advanced are the skills of the experienced listener, that it is, for many, a hobby within a hobby. Working to a careful listening plan the keen short-wave listener (SWL) can spend hours searching out stations from, say, Central America or the Far East, that are normally considered to be inaudible here in Europe. Carefully presented reception reports can be sent off to those stations and will often result in all sorts of interesting material being sent back as an acknowledgement.

The larger stations provide their regular listeners with schedules of coming events and many offer 'DX' programmes in which the letters from listeners are read out or answered over the air.

What is 'DX'? The term

refers to radio stations which are far away or as 'rare DX' are very difficult to hear, perhaps because they transmit at times that make reception an unusual event.

Listening to the radio amateurs of the world is a must if you are really thinking

Short-wave broadcasting station PHOTO: BBC

33

Short-wave stations offer interesting glimpses into other countries and their culture

PHOTO: BBC

your local broadcast station.

The tuning and adjustment of a sensitive short-wave radio to 'pull in' the required signals is not difficult but does require practice. Signals are packed together in narrow segments at specific spots on your dial. You will find the various services, like amateurs, broadcasting, shipping and aircraft, all have their own bands of frequencies and many other services 'fill in' between these bands.

With a little experience, you will know where on the bands to look and how to identify just who or what you are listening to at any given time.

The amateur bands that you will find marked on the dials of some communication receivers are on 80, 40, 20, 15 and 10 metres wavelength (3·5MHz, 7MHz, 14MHz, 21MHz and 28MHz are the corresponding frequencies), but there are several other short-wave amateur bands available. In the table opposite, we take a brief look at the most popular. Note that conditions on short-wave bands are usually dependent to some extent on how many sunspots there are on the Sun, and this varies in an 11-year 'sunspot cycle'.

of taking out a licence to transmit. Your skills as a future radio operator will be much improved if you spend your early days listening to experienced amateurs enjoying their hobby. You will begin to understand the various types of operating and contacts. Your knowledge of rare callsigns and the best time of day to contact the different regions of the world will all be based upon your developing expertise as a listener.

Listening on short waves, and indeed on the very short waves (VHF and UHF), requires quite a different method of approach to that needed to listen to

Most amateurs will be speaking in English, or a somewhat abbreviated version of English. Much of their

RECEIVING STATION LOG															
Date 19 _91_	Time GMT	Band (MHz)	Call-sign	R	S	T	MODE	calling / working Station			given		received		REMARKS:
									R	S	T	R	S	T	
25/9	2016	21	PY9QBZ	5	7	9	CW		G2MNO		5	8	9	5	7	9
"	2023	"	LU4QRD	5	9	9	CW	G2MNC							
"	2049	14	PTØGX	5	7		SSb		DL7QB		5	8		5	9

A few entries from a typical SWL log

THE AMATEUR BANDS

160 metres (1.810-2MHz)
This band, affectionately known as 'Top Band', is the lowest-frequency band available to amateurs, and is shared with coastal shipping as well as other professional stations. During the day, you can hear local stations up to 100km away, with more-distant stations coming in at night. In the UK, Novice licensees are permitted to use 50kHz of the band (1.950-2.000MHz) for voice communication.

80 metres (3.5-3.8MHz)
This is a band that amateurs share with professional stations, so not every signal you hear is from amateurs. It is mainly used for contacts with other British stations during the day, and you will probably be able to hear strong signals from amateurs in your town. In the evening, you should be able to hear further afield, including the Continent.

40 metres (7-7.1MHz)
Although this band is not shared with broadcasting stations, at night the level of interference from them is high. Only the better receivers will yield a good selection of amateur signals. Reception is highly variable, with intercontinental communication possible in the most favourable conditions.

20 metres (14.0-14.35MHz)
The 20m band is the most rewarding band to listen to if you want to hear stations from all over the world. It is usually at its best during dawn and dusk, but you should be able to hear long-distance (DX) stations almost anytime in the day, and during the evening as well at the peak of the sunspot cycle. The band is very crowded at weekends, with many American stations audible during the afternoon.

15 metres (21.0-21.45MHz)
This band is almost as good as the 20m band for DX, although not as crowded. Spring and autumn are the best times at the peak of the sunspot cycle. It is often best in a south-west direction from the UK, so listen out for South American stations just before dusk. The band usually fades out after nightfall.

10 metres (28-29.7MHz)
At the peak of the sunspot cycle, this band is full of DX signals from all over the world; in the low sunspot years, it is quiet, with only local stations. As with the 15m band, it is good for South America and Africa, and fades out shortly after dusk. In the UK, Novice licensees are permitted to use 28.3-28.5MHz for voice communication.

conversation will seem a little confusing at first because they rely on the use of codes to convey information as quickly as possible. An explanation of these codes is given in a later chapter. Of course, you will find, say, French, German, Spanish, Italian and Russian stations working each other in their own tongues – very useful if you are studying a second language.

It is a good idea to keep a log of all you hear. The date, time, frequency and the callsign of the station will be important. Notes on particular items of interest, such as the operator's name and location, or 'QTH' as it is called, can be

extended to include details of his transmitter, power and aerials, all of which will help you build up your understanding and skill as a radio amateur.

The illustration on the left shows a few entries from a typical SWL log. Ready-printed log books are available from the RSGB, or you can rule up your own to suit yourself in an old exercise book.

Many magazines, such as *Radio Communication* (the journal of the Radio Society of Great Britain) carry articles on what to listen for and when, as well as information and reviews on the latest receivers.

CHAPTER 7

Your first short-wave receiver

THERE are various ways in which you can equip yourself for short-wave listening.

It may be possible for you to borrow a small communication receiver for a while from a friendly local amateur who, with a bit of luck, will teach you how to operate the controls. He or she will certainly be able to advise you and give you a head start over those who have to find out for themselves. The Radio Society of Great Britain can provide you with a list of clubs in your area who will help the beginner. Lots of Scout and Guide groups also have radio activities. Such assistance may well be available within your neighbourhood and will almost certainly enable you to visit a

working station and see for yourself how it is done!

For the absolute beginner, the thought of building a short-wave radio may be somewhat daunting. Nevertheless, this is how many start, with a considerable degree of success due to the availability of simple kits of parts. The kits most suitable for your first venture come with detailed instructions on just what to do and how to do it. Even though you may not yet understand the circuitry or recognise all the different electronic components, it is amazing how well a few pictures and step-by-step instructions can help you through the project.

Most kit suppliers appreciate the

A kit receiver for the 80, 40 and 20m amateur bands   PHOTO: LAKE ELECTRONICS

A low-cost communication receiver

PHOTO: LOWE ELECTRONICS

need to help the beginner and will do all they can to ensure your success, including a little 'trouble shooting' back at their factory should you experience difficulty in getting your kit up and running.

For short waves, it is essential that all the wiring and connections in the receiver should be soldered. For those who have no previous experience with a miniature soldering iron, a glance through the notes in appendix 1 will soon set your mind at rest. Like everything else there is a simple knack for doing it right first time, every time.

To minimise any difficulty, and to get going as cheaply as possible, it is recommended that you first build a simple kit that will receive amateurs on just one of the bands. Such a set can be equally as sensitive as a more advanced, multiband model but has the great advantage that it does not need the switches and the rather complicated wiring necessary to cover all the short waves from 80 to 10 metres.

Should you have already progressed through the early construction stages or, perhaps, feel unable to make your own receiver, then you will obviously need to acquire a ready-made commercial set.

The market for short-wave and amateur band equipment is very well supported by manufacturers all over the world and their range covers just about every conceivable type of listening you may require. A strong second-hand market is open to anyone who cares to browse through the small advertisements in the radio magazines and some real bargains can be found.

Your local club will have surplus equipment sales where members dispose of unwanted items. These sales are always the most popular and best attended events on the club calendar. The 'gear' is usually auctioned amidst much wit and hilarity. Prices are often ridiculously low, with most of the 'lots'

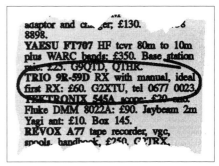

You can often find a bargain hunting through the small ads

A large amateur radio dealer

PHOTO: LOWE ELECTRONICS

changing hands for a tiny fraction of their market value.

To buy yourself a new or second-hand communication receiver, you will need to decide first how much you can afford to pay and then what it is that you intend to do with it.

Brand-new sets can cost from a few hundred to many thousands of pounds. They can be fairly simple but effective designs for use on amateur bands or an 'all-singing-all-dancing' receiver with lots of push buttons and knobs, and capable of high performance in the hands of an expert.

It is advisable to choose a fairly simple model to get you started. Later, it can be traded in for a more advanced receiver or, as is usually the case, kept for many years as a standby set.

Rely on the advice of your amateur radio retailer and reveal to him that you are a beginner and need help. He will usually do all he can to see that you are properly set-up and will be hoping to retain your custom as you progress in the hobby. You will probably become firm friends. Even the purchase of your bits and pieces on a Saturday morning tends to become a highly sociable and enjoyable experience.

Should you live too far from your nearest retail shop, then the phone and mail order will see you through. Such is the friendly competition within the amateur radio trade, that retailers have perfected the ability to serve their customers at any distance whilst keeping a very personal relationship. After all, they will probably work you on the air before long and will certainly be looking forward to meeting you at one of the exhibitions where they set up their stands.

When buying a ready-made set you will obviously have some operating instructions, although perhaps this manual may be missing in the case of a second-hand set. In any case, it might be helpful if you read the next chapter so that you know which are the right knobs to turn and what to expect when you turn them.

CHAPTER 8

Operating a short-wave receiver

T O get the best reception from a short-wave receiver, the new listener needs to have some idea of the function of each of the basic controls on the front and back panels.

Sitting in front of a short-wave set for the first time, you may feel a little bewildered by the apparent complexity of the many knobs, switches and push buttons. However, they all have a useful function, and you will be amazed at how quickly you become accustomed to using the right ones to tune in and hold the signal you require. Most factory-built receivers will come to you with a handbook showing how to connect the set up and operate it. Always read and try to understand these instructions before you switch on.

As you may be starting out with a simple model or your homebrew kit, let us take a look at a typical example.

Simple receiver

First, locate the terminal or sockets that are marked 'Aerial' (or 'ANT' for antenna). If there are several aerial points, they are likely to be marked 'Dipole', 'Coax', 'Balanced' or 'Long Wire'. Check your handbook and, using a suitable plug or perhaps one of your crocodile clips, connect up your wire aerial to the terminal marked 'LW' for Long Wire if there is one. If you have an earth, it goes to the terminal marked 'Ground'. The aerial you used for the crystal set should do fine.

If the receiver is powered by battery, check that you have a good set of

batteries in the holder. If operated from the mains, make sure that your plug has a low-rated fuse in it, usually one or three amps. Plug in, and you are ready to go.

Hopefully you will have a built-in loudspeaker. If not, then your headphones will need connecting or plugging into the socket marked 'Phones'. By the way, the earpiece you used for the crystal set is not suitable – use ordinary hi-fi headphones, or communications headphones if you can afford them.

Some sets made for the international market may have the sockets for aerial and earth marked with the symbols that we met in chapter 4.

1. ON/OFF switch
The front panel ON/OFF control may be marked 'Power'. It may also be either a straightforward switch, or form part of the volume control and require turning on by rotating the knob clockwise. You will feel it click on and, with a bit of luck, the dial lights should come on and the receiver should burst into life.

2. Volume controls
There are usually two volume controls on a communication receiver. They are marked 'RF Gain' and 'AF Gain'. RF Gain (radio frequency gain) adjusts the level of amplification for the 'front-end' of the circuit. The AF Gain (audio frequency gain) is the same as the simple volume control you would find on all radios and allows you to set the sound at a comfortable level.

A communication receiver showing the main controls

PHOTO: THANET ELECTRONICS

3. Tuning control

To search across the dial there is the familiar tuning control, that could well have two knobs on the one shaft. The rear and larger control enables you to tune rapidly to a required band and the smaller one is geared right down so that the operator can fine tune to an exact frequency and centre on the signal perfectly.

On a simple homebrew model, you will probably have only one tuning control and one gain control. You will need to practise setting them carefully and gently, using just your finger tips and a keen ear.

Some receivers will put the fine tune or 'bandspread' knob as a separate control. It may also be marked 'RIT' which means 'receiver incremental tuning' – a technical way of saying that the control will allow you to tune just a little way either side of the listening frequency.

4. Band change

The 'band change' control is usually a rotating knob or pointer that switches to different tuned circuits – yes, they are just like the one in your crystal set but in miniature. Each of the coils and trimming capacitors is set to cover a part of the short-wave bands when tuned with the main capacitors that are varied when you spin round your tuning control.

5. BFO or mode switch

Some sets will have a BFO control and this should be switched off to listen in to the normal broadcasting station – you just do not need it. However, to resolve a morse transmission the beat frequency oscillator is used to mix together an internal signal with the incoming signal to provide you with a 'beat' note in your loudspeaker. If your BFO is variable, you can adjust the tone of the note to suit your preference for a treble or a bass sound. For speech, the majority of amateur stations on the short-wave bands use a method or 'mode' of transmission called 'SSB' (single sideband).

Don't worry about what this means exactly at this stage, except to understand that it is a means of improving the performance of a transmission and also of having many more stations on a crowded band.

If you are tuning in an SSB station without the BFO switched on, the speech will sound distorted and will sound like a pretty fair impersonation of Donald Duck! Switch on the BFO control, fine tune the speech very carefully and you will hear the words loud and clear. You may need to turn the RF gain control down for best results.

The more modern communication receivers have done away with a separate BFO tuning control and have tidied up the selection of 'mode' or method of reception. By turning a switch you can choose a variety of modes. Your receiver may offer:

AM –This stands for 'amplitude modulation', another technical term that describes the type of speech transmission that is used by broadcasting stations on long, medium and short waves but not VHF.

CW – These initials stand for 'continuous wave' and mean that you are ready to listen to ordinary Morse code. The term makes sense when you realise that if the operator of a transmitter holds his key down, the set just sends out a continuous radio wave – no speech, no 'modulation', just a simple signal that can be keyed into morse characters. You will find most CW at the lower frequency end of every amateur band.

USB – Stands for 'upper sideband'. This is the form of SSB, or 'single sideband' speech transmission, normally selected for operating on the 20, 15 and 10 metre bands. It is also is used on the new amateur bands of 17 and 12 metres (18MHz and 24MHz) that are alive with stations enjoying the fun of operating on these excellent long-distance frequencies.

LSB – Yes, this is 'lower sideband'.

Choose this switch position for listening on 160, 80 and 40 metres.

RTTY – These letters stand for 'radio teletype'. Again, this is the mode where messages are typed out on a keyboard and transmitted to appear on the screen of a TV monitor or computer screen. There are other computer-orientated modes, of which we will say a little more in a later chapter.

FM – You will probably already recognise the letters for 'frequency modulation'. This is the type of speech or music transmission used most frequently on the VHF/FM bands of your personal transistor set. There are a few FM signals to be found on the 10 metre amateur band but FM is not really suitable for the crowded short-wave bands because it uses up too much space.

6. Signal strength meter
Most communication sets have a useful way of displaying the relative strength of the incoming signal to help you tune it in correctly. It is usually a meter, consisting of a moving pointer in front of a calibrated scale or a line of small lights that come on one after the other as the strength of the signal improves. The meter is calibrated in 'S' units and decibels. Don't worry what these words mean! Just remember that it is called an 'S meter' and can help you log and report a signal level in units from one to nine.

Of course you may not have all of these controls on your set. However, if the receiver is a really expensive model they will all be there, together with a whole lot more.

Once you become experienced, you will find that little luxuries like a filter and a noise blanker to cut down interference, a calibrator to check your precise frequency and a rather useful control called 'bandpass tuning' are almost essential.

Memories

Push-button 'memories' are now an important feature of short-wave receivers. Just like the memory button on your calculator, the memory banks of a radio will hold set frequencies for future reference. They can be programmed to suit your needs and are quite separate from the normal tuning action of the receiver; they become very useful when you are constantly checking favourite stations or listening on specific channels.

Pocket VHF and UHF receivers

Many amateurs use pocket-size portable receivers to listen to the 2 metre VHF and the 70 centimetre UHF bands. These amateur frequencies carry FM and USB signals as well as CW. Being extremely compact, the controls on these sets are tiny, and somewhat limited compared with their bigger brothers, but still perform the same functions.

These portables are amazingly sensitive, even when using their built-in telescopic aerials or a 'rubber duck'. "What's a rubber duck?", you ask. It's just

A powerful AM/FM communication receiver covering VHF/ UHF
PHOTO: NEVADA COMMUNICATIONS

A world broadcast receiver. Note the BFO control, top right

PHOTO: PHILLIPS

the fun name given to the flexible aerial that screws into the top of the set.

Broadcast receivers

With the ever increasing interest in overseas travel, a number of the manufacturers of portable sets have improved their long, medium and short-wave radios by building in a BFO or a control for SSB. For general broadcast listening these sets are excellent and are very sensitive. Their performance on the amateur bands is adequate enough to receive strong signals but, due to their design, the tuning dial and 'selectivity' is somewhat restricted for serious use and the reception of weak signals on a crowded band is unsatisfactory when compared with a communication model.

Having read this far and, hopefully, had the opportunity to operate a good receiver, you will realise that it has taken rather longer to write these explanations than it has for you to understand their significance.

Now it is down to you to get the feel of the receiver and to enjoy the unique experience of short-wave listening, where it is often the case that a station in Australia is far stronger than another in Europe.

Just hearing the signals from people in their homes all over the world coming to you, right there in your own shack, will turn your thoughts inevitably to the possibility of transmitting your own signals, the need to obtain an amateur licence and the great day when you are issued with your own callsign.

CHAPTER 9

Callsigns, codes and abbreviations

AS you have already seen, every amateur station in the world has its own, unique callsign, which is sent at the beginning and end of each transmission. Amateur calls consist of a series of letters and figures that are so arranged as to indicate the country of origin and, in many cases, the area within that country or territory.

Here in the UK, most calls start with the letter G followed by a figure and either two or three letters. Calls that have an extra letter after the G are allocated to stations operating in areas of the UK other than England, for example:

G3QQQ is used in England
GW3QQQ for Wales
GM3QQQ for Scotland
GI3QQQ for Northern Ireland
GD3QQQ for the Isle of Man
GJ3QQQ for Jersey
GU3QQQ for Guernsey

Amateurs in the UK holding a Novice Licence use callsigns starting with the figure '2', followed by a letter, another number and three letters, eg 2E1QQQ. As with the G callsigns, the second character varies, depending on where in the UK operation takes place:

2E1QQQ is used in England
2W1QQQ for Wales

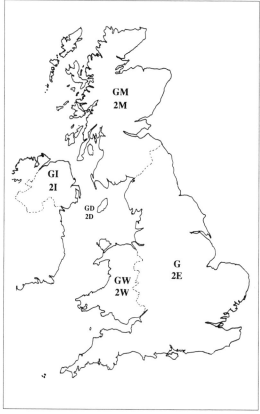

The callsign areas of the UK

2M1QQQ for Scotland
2I1QQQ for Northern Ireland
2D1QQQ for the Isle of Man
2J1QQQ for Jersey
2U1QQQ for Guernsey

The third character, a number, denotes the class of licence. Novice Licence

SOME AMATEUR CALLSIGN PREFIXES

Australia	VK
Belgium	ON
Brazil	PY
Denmark	OZ
France	F
Germany	DJ, DK, DL, DM
Holland	PA
Irish Republic	EI
Italy	I
Norway	LA
Spain	EA
Sweden	SM
Switzerland	HB
USA	W, K, N, A
USSR	U, R
Yugoslavia	YU

THE RST CODE

R for readability
R1   Unreadable
R2   Barely readable
R3   Readable with difficulty
R4   Readable with almost no difficulty
R5   Perfectly readable

S for signal strength
S1   Faint signals
S2   Very weak signals
S3   Weak signals
S4   Fair signals
S5   Fairly good signals
S6   Good signals
S7   Moderately strong signals
S8   Strong signals
S9   Very strong signals

T for CW tone
T1   Rough hissing sound
T2   Very rough note
T3   Rough note
T4   Rather rough note
T5   Musically modulated note
T6   Modulated note with trace of whistle
T7   Musical note with ripple
T8   Musical note with trace of ripple
T9   Pure musical note

Class A licences use 0, 2, 3 or 4, and Class B use 1, 6, 7 or 8, eg 2E1QQQ is a Novice Class B callsign (see chapter 12 for more information about the differences between Class A and Class B licences).

Should you hear an extra letter at the end of the callsign, eg G3JNB/P, this would indicate that the call was being used away from the normal location, say, from a field operation or at some-one else's house.

If you were to hear a call such as G3JNB/M then you would know immediately that it was operating from a car or boat. The call G3JNB/MM tells you that the station is a maritime mobile operating on board a ship on the open sea.

These prefixes and suffixes apply to all amateur stations when operating away from their usual location.

As you become accustomed to listening on the amateur bands, you will start to recognise where the stations are located. The Americans have prefixes beginning with W, K, N and A. Most Russians use the letter U or R for USSR, the French use F and the Germans DJ, DL and DK (see above table for a more complete list). As in the

UK, there are also calls that start with a figure, such as 5B4 for Cyprus and 9H for Malta.

There are many variations on these calls and a more comprehensive list will be found in other RSGB publications.

The RST code

Codes form a useful role in the communications between stations, speeding up the contact and helping to ensure clarity in a conversation between people who are not fluent in the other's language.

When reporting a station's signal, either over the air or when submitting a written report, the amateur RST code is used. The letters RST stand for 'readability, signal strength and tone'. This code is short and conveys everything the transmitting station needs to know (see the table).

The tone figure is not used for speech transmissions. For example, if you hear a station say "You are 5 and 9", that means the other station is being received loud and clear.

For morse code signals (see later), the full three-figure code is used. A report on a perfectly readable, exceptionally strong and pure morse signal would be simply '599'. With a less strong signal and perhaps less readability, the report might be 469.

Phonetics

Imagine that an amateur station is trying to read a weak speech signal through noise and other signals. The operator simply must get that callsign in the log. Unfortunately, many letters can sound the same over a microphone. Compare 'M' and 'N' or 'B' and 'P', for example.

To avoid this problem, a 'phonetic' alphabet has therefore been created that is instantly recognisable in all languages (see table).

For example, the amateur callsign G3ABC would be pronounced:

"Golf Three Alpha Bravo Charlie"

Some other phonetic alphabets will be heard on the amateur bands but this is the recommended one.

The morse code

This is used by amateur stations to send transmissions using a morse key. It is a straightforward combination of dots, dashes and spaces, and is set out in the table on the next page.

The secret of learning morse is to 'hear' it as sounds (for example, di-dah) rather than to 'see' it as a set of dots and dashes on paper. For example, one of the most frequent morse 'sounds' you will be receiving will be the code 'CQ' which stands for 'General Call'. The letters sound like this:

THE PHONETIC ALPHABET	
A	Alpha
B	Bravo
C	Charlie
D	Delta
E	Echo
F	Foxtrot
G	Golf
H	Hotel
I	India
J	Juliet
K	Kilo
L	Lima
M	Mike
N	November
O	Oscar
P	Papa
Q	Quebec
R	Romeo
S	Sierra
T	Tango
U	Uniform
V	Victor
W	Whiskey
X	X-Ray
Y	Yankee
Z	Zulu

C dah-di-dah-dit
Q dah-dah-di-dah

If you say these sounds to yourself over and over again you will begin to recognise them on the air.

The RSGB publishes an excellent booklet called *Morse Code for the Radio Amateur* and a morse instruction tape which will teach you to read up to speeds of five words a minute. There are slow morse transmissions on the air, organised by the RSGB, designed to help all listeners work up their speed and, of course, tuition at many local clubs and classes.

It helps to learn the code if you have a friend to work with and to be able to practise regularly together. Alternatively, there are computer programs that will help you to learn quickly. A few minutes

THE MORSE CODE

A	di-dah	V	di-di-di-dah
B	dah-di-di-dit	W	di-dah-dah
C	dah-di-dah-dit	X	dah-di-di-dah
D	dah-di-dit	Y	dah-di-dah-dah
E	dit	Z	dah-dah-di-dit
F	di-di-dah-dit		
G	dah-dah-dit	1	di-dah-dah-dah-dah
H	di-di-di-dit	2	di-di-dah-dah-dah
I	di-dit	3	di-di-di-dah-dah
J	di-dah-dah-dah	4	di-di-di-di-dah
K	dah-di-dah	5	di-di-di-di-dit
L	di-dah-di-dit	6	dah-di-di-di-dit
M	dah-dah	7	dah-dah-di-di-dit
N	dah-dit	8	dah-dah-dah-di-dit
O	dah-dah-dah	9	dah-dah-dah-dah-dit
P	di-dah-dah-dit	0	dah-dah-dah-dah-dah
Q	dah-dah-di-dah		
R	di-dah-dit	End of phrase	dah-di-di-di-dah
S	di-di-dit	End of transmission	di-dah-di-dah-dit
T	dah	End of contact	di-di-di-dah-di-dah
U	di-di-dah		

Plenty of practice is essential when learning morse

THE Q CODE	
QRM	I am suffering interference (from other stations)
QRN	I am suffering interference (from static)
QRQ	Send faster
QRS	Send slower
QRT	Stop sending or close down
QRX	Wait
QRZ	You are being called by ...
QSB	Your signals are fading
QSL	I received the information
QSO	Radio contact
QSY	Change frequency
QTH	My location is ...

ABBREVIATIONS	
AGN	Again
BCNU	Be seeing you
CONDX	Conditions
CQ	Calling any station
DE	From
DX	Rare or long distance station
ES	And
FER	For
HI	Laughter
HR	Here
NR	Number or near
OM	'Old man'
R	Roger or received
RX	Receiver
SRI	Sorry
TX	Transmitter
TNX	Thanks
UR	Your
WX	Weather
XYL	Wife
YL	Young lady
73	Best wishes
88	Love and kisses

a day, rather than an occasional long session, will soon 'program' your brain to interpret the sounds correctly. Although it is tempting to use a morse key straight away when you first start learning, the advice from the experts is to leave the key alone until you can receive fairly accurately. Then, when you start to use a key, your morse should have a smooth rhythm.

To help you to learn to send the characters, a morse practice set is a must. This can be a simple buzzer wired up with a battery and a morse key. Maplin sell a practice oscillator kit at a very reasonable price.

The Q Code

The international Q Code consists of three letters, the first one of which is always the letter Q. There is a whole list of meanings that cover nearly every conceivable eventuality for morse signalling in 'shorthand'. Amateurs have selected and adapted the meaning of some of the more useful Q code abbreviations to suit themselves and you will hear them constantly being used on the bands. Some examples are shown in the table.

A question mark after the code turns the message into a question. Thus

'QSL?' stands for "Did you receive that information OK?" and 'QRZ?' means "Who is calling me?" Some of the frequently used Q codes are sometimes used as parts of speech, eg 'QRM' means 'interference from other stations'.

You will soon recognise these letters for their true meaning, and can practise them when you learn your morse or are listening to your local stations chatting to each other on the key.

Abbreviations

To speed up morse code contacts, abbreviations are used. Many of them are fairly obvious and others tend to be easily remembered when operators have the need to use them frequently. A few samples are given in the table.

You will find all of these, together with the various codes and a host of valuable information, in the *RSGB Amateur Radio Call Book* and in other RSGB publications.

CHAPTER 10

How to collect QSL cards

YOU will remember that QSL stands for an acknowledgement. Most stations have a 'QSL card' specially printed to use as a written confirmation of a contact or to acknowledge a listener's report.

These cards display the station's callsign, its location, details of the equipment and have a space for a report to be written in by the operator.

Once you become a licensed operator you may send and receive hundreds of QSL cards and it is an interesting aspect of the hobby to collect them, in the same way that you may collect postage stamps. Indeed, there are special awards and certificates to be won by submitting the appropriate number of cards to the Radio Society of Great Britain or other societies.

As a listener, you can start your QSL collection by sending detailed reports to stations that you hear. To be successful in this aspect of the hobby, your reports really do have to have a genuine value to the operator you send them to, and you would be well advised to read up the whole technique of preparing such reports if you are going to chase those rare ones.

To avoid paying out large sums on postage to stations all over the world, membership of your country's national society usually entitles you to send out your cards through a QSL Bureau. You sort out the cards and post them in bulk to the Bureau Manager who forwards them to the bureau in the overseas territory. Your incoming cards also pass through these organisations and eventually arrive back in the post in the stamped addressed envelopes that you have deposited at the RSGB QSL Bureau. Of course, this takes time and, in urgent cases, you may choose to mail your QSL card and perhaps a covering letter direct to the station in far-off lands.

The majority of callsigns and corresponding addresses are listed in national and international directories that are published annually, just like telephone directories. Here in the UK, the national directory is the *RSGB Amateur Radio Call Book*.

Perhaps, one day soon, your own call and your 'QTH' may be eagerly looked up by another amateur anxious to write to you telling of your outstanding signal down there on the Gold Coast!

G2MNO

S. BROWN, 22 SELBY GARDENS, LONDON NW14 8SE, ENGLAND

RADIO	DATE	GMT	MHz	2-WAY	RST
2E4QAB	22.10.91	1732	3.570	CW	579

RX/TX ....TS120..........   (PSE/TNX QSL DIRECT/VIA RSGB)

ANT .....Long wire.............

73 ....Steve............................

A typical QSL card confirming a contact

A shack wall showing the enormous range of styles of QSL cards

CHAPTER 11

Learning the language of radio – 2

HERE we are, six chapters on from the first time you checked up on your knowledge of the language of your new hobby. Shall we take another list of terms to show you how much you now know?

AF Gain or Audio Volume control.

AM Amplitude modulation like normal broadcast speech and music other than FM on the VHF bands.

Bandchange Switching of tuned circuits to another wave band.

Bandspread Fine tuning control.

Coax Coaxial cable consisting of a centre wire insulated from an outer screen of metal braid. Your TV set is connected to its aerial by a coax cable.

CW Continuous wave or morse transmission.

Dipole A centre-fed aerial cut to suit a specific frequency.

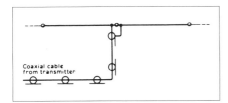

A dipole aerial fed by coaxial cable. It is usually only used on a single band

DX Long-distance or rare station

FM Frequency modulation. High-quality speech and music broadcasts on VHF bands use this mode.

Long wire Usually a long single wire aerial connected to the radio at one end.

Phonetics International code using words for letters.

Q code International code for standard messages.

QSL card A written confirmation of contact.

RIT Receiver incremental tuning; tuned just a little either side of the main dial frequency.

RST Code for readability, signal strength and tone.

RTTY Radio teletype.

RF gain Volume control operating at the beginning of a receiver circuit to control the level of signal before detection.

S meter Visual indicator of signal strength.

So there you are, a few more words that you now know and can use freely in your own conversations down at the club. There are lots more to come but you will pick them up as you go along.

CHAPTER 12

How to get your amateur licence

I N chapter 3 you will have read how necessary it is for all of the world's radio stations, both amateur and professional, to be licensed by the authorities. The amateurs that you have been listening to have all 'qualified' for their callsigns by taking a test to prove their knowledge of basic radio theory and practice, plus the fact that they understand the legal aspects of holding a licence.

Over one and a half million licensees all over the world have passed their Radio Amateurs' Examination by learning all that is required from the various books, manuals and magazines published to help them win that coveted callsign and a full licence.

In the USA and a number of other countries, it is recognised that to encourage the beginner a simplified 'way in' proves to be an ideal introduction to

---

Validation Document
Document de Validation
Gültigkeitserklärung

dti

Radiocommunications Division

United Kingdom of Great Britain and Northern Ireland, the Channel Islands and the Isle of Man
Royaume-Uni de Grande Bretagne et d'Irlande du Nord, les Iles Anglo-Normandes et l'Ile de Man
Für das Vereinigte Königreich von Grossbritannien und Nordirland, die Kanalinseln und die Isle of Man

Wireless Telegraphy Act 1949
Loi sur la Télégraphie sans Fil de 1949
Gesetz über drahtlose Telegrafie 1949

Amateur Radio Licence (A)	CEPT Equivalent Licence Class	1
Licence de Radio Amateur	Classe de Licence Equivalente CEPT	
Amateurfunkgenehmigung	gleichwertige CEPT-Genehmigungsklasse	

(a)	Licensee's Name		(b)	Call Sign	
(a)	Nom du Titulaire		(b)	Indicatif d'appel	
(a)	Name des Inhabers	MR S BROWN	(b)	Rufzeichen	G2MNO

(c)	Mailing Address		(d)	Main Station Address	
(c)	Adresse Postale	22 SELBY GARDENS	(d)	Adresse de la station principale	22 SELBY GARDENS
(c)	Postanschrift	LONDON NW14 8SE	(d)	Anschrift der Hauptstation	LONDON NW14 8SE

(e)	Date for Renewal	03.03.1992
(e)	Date de renouvellement	
(e)	Erneuerungsdatum	

This licence (the "Licence") granted on   03.03.1949   ("Date of Issue") by the Secretary of State for Trade and Industry to the Licensee named in paragraph (a) above under section 1 of the Wireless Telegraphy Act 1949 authorises the Licensee to establish, instal and use sending and receiving apparatus for wireless telegraphy at the Station [as defined in sub-clause 1(10)] in accordance with the Terms and Limitations Booklet BR68 which is incorporated into and forms a part of this Licence.

La présente licence (la "Licence") accordée le ("Date d'émission") par le Ministre du Commerce et de l'Industrie au Titulaire nomme au paragraphe (a) ci-dessus en application de la section 1 de la Loi de 1949 sur la Télégraphie sans Fil autorise le Titulaire à etablir, installer et utiliser un appareil d'emission et de reception pour la Télégraphie sans Fil a la station [definie au paragraphe 1(10)] conformement au Receuil des Termes et Limitations BR68 qui est incorpore dans la presente Licence et en fait partie integrante.

Diese Genehmigung (die "Genehmigung"), die dem in Paragraph (a) vorstehend genannten Lizenzinhaber aufgrund des Abschnitts 1 des Gesetzes uber drahtlose Telegrafie 1949 am ("Datum der Erteilung") von dem Minister für Handel und Industrie erteilt wurde, berechtigt den Inhaber zur Einrichtung, Installierung und Verwendung von Sende -und Empfangsgeräten für drahtlose Telegrafie an der [in Unterklausel 1(10) definierten] Station im Einklang mit der Broschure BR68 über Bedingungen und Einschränkungen, die in diese Genehmigung einbezogen ist und einen Bestandteil hiervon bildet.

Part of an amateur radio licence

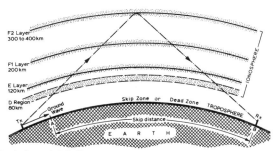

Fig 7.2: Reflection of radio waves by ionised layers

Ground-wave propagation

In ground-wave propagation, the radiated wave follows the surface of the earth. It is the major mode of propagation for frequencies up to 1MHz to 2MHz. Attenuation of the ground wave increases very rapidly above 2MHz and it may extend for only a few kilometres at frequencies of the order of 15-20MHz. At very low frequencies the attenuation decreases to such an extent that reliable world-wide communication is possible at all times. The ground wave is not so affected by atmospheric effects or time of day as other modes, particularly at frequencies below about 500kHz.

Ionospheric propagation

Ionospheric propagation is the refraction (ie bending) and hence reflection of radio waves back to earth by layers of ionised gases as shown in fig 7.2. It is the normal mode of propagation over the frequency range of about 1MHz to 30MHz.

These layers are the F2 layer (height 300 - 400km); F1 layer (about 200km) and the E layer (about 120km). At night and in mid winter, the F1 and F2 layers tend to combine into a single layer at a height of about 250km. At about 80km there is a much less distinct layer which is generally known as the D region.

The ionised layers are the result of the ionisation of the oxygen, nitrogen and nitric oxide in the rarified atmosphere at these heights by X- and ultra-violet radiation of various wavelengths which comes from the sun.

When these gases are ionised the molecules split up into ions and free electrons, and recombine after sunset. This whole region is therefore known as the "ionosphere".

The solar radiation which causes the ionisation is continually varying; hence the degree of ionisation varies considerably according to season and time of day. It has also been found that the degree of ionisation is affected by the number of sunspots.

The number of sunspots varies cyclically, with maximum activity occurring at about 11-year intervals. Thus maximum ionisation occurs at the same intervals. The next maximum may not occur until 1990-1.As the frequency of the radio wave increases, a greater level of ionisation is needed to cause reflection. The F2 layer normally has the greatest ionisation and so it is the F2 layer which reflects the highest frequencies which have passed through the lower layers. It is seen from fig 7.2 that it is this layer which reflects back to earth at the greatest distance from the transmitter. Therefore it is the characteristics of the F2 layer which are of most interest and significance in long-distance communication. The major significance of the D region is that it absorbs the frequencies under discussion in abnormal circumstances.

The maximum frequency which is reflected in the ionosphere is known as the "maximum usable frequency" (muf). This frequency depends on many factors, ie season, time of day, path latitude and state of the sunspot cycle. Signals above the muf pass through the F2 layer and are lost in space. The curves of figs 7.3 - 7.6 indicate the likely variation of the muf, ie.

1) The peak value of the muf generally occurs between 10.00 and 16.00 hours.
2) Peak values are much higher at sunspot maximum than at the sunspot minimum.
3) Peak values are much higher in the winter than in the summer.
4) There is a much larger variation in the muf over the day in the winter than in the summer.
5) Comparison of figs 7.3 and 7.5 shows that the muf is higher in a North-South direction, eg the London-Cape Town path than in an East-West direction, eg London-New York path. Figs 7.4 and 7.6 show muf variations for intermediate directions.

Around the sunspot maximum, the muf may exceed 50MHz for short periods, but at the minimum it rarely exceeds 25MHz.

A page from the RSGB *Radio Amateurs' Examination Manual*

the hobby. Their 'Novice Licence' is becoming increasingly popular, requiring a much simpler theory test and a morse test of five words a minute (wpm) rather than the usual 12wpm. During 1989 the RSGB entered into lengthy discussions with the Radiocommunications Agency

of the DTI with a view to issuing a new type of licence in the UK – the Amateur Radio Novice Licence. This became available in 1991.

The idea of the Novice Licence is to provide an easy introduction into amateur radio. It will offer a stepping stone towards a full Class A or B Licence and is based on a solid foundation of practical training. Beginners of all ages are able to qualify for a Novice Licence.

To obtain either type of Novice Licence (Class A or B) you will first have to complete 30 hours of training, spread over maybe three months, on an RSGB-approved training course. These are held up and down the country and a list of instructors in your county can be obtained by sending a stamped self-addressed envelope to the Novice Section at RSGB HQ.

On successful completion of the training, you can sit a straightforward multiple-choice examination organised by the City and Guilds of London Institute at the address below.

City and Guilds of London Institute
46 Britannia Street
London
WC1X 9RG

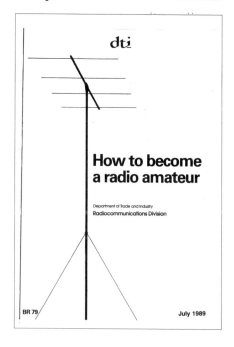

How to become a radio amateur

Department of Trade and Industry
Radiocommunications Division

BR 79   July 1989

If you pass this examination the Class B Novice Licence is yours. You can now operate with low power on certain allocated frequencies on the VHF and UHF bands.

If, however, you would like to operate on the HF bands as well (see chapter 6) then you will need to pass a morse test at 5wpm. A beginner's morse tape (up to 5wpm) can be obtained from the RSGB, along with a list of morse test centres near you.

If you are totally new to the world of radio communication, you will obviously choose to go for your Novice Licence. On the other hand, if you already know quite a bit about electronics and are aged 14 years or over, then you may decide to sit for the City and Guilds Radio Amateurs' Examination right away or after a period of study to brush up your theory and to learn the regulations.

The Radiocommunications Agency has an excellent publication, *How to*

Become a Radio Amateur, that sets out just what is required to qualify for the full licence. It is available free from this address:

The Radiocommunications Agency
Waterloo Bridge House
Waterloo Road
London
SE1 8UA

The Radio Society of Great Britain will be publishing a similar pamphlet for the Novice Licence.

The Novice Licence will be free to those under 21.

Don't forget that once you have made up your mind to 'get on the air', you will find all the help you need at your local club. To help put you in touch with the club nearest to your home, just write, enclosing a stamped self-addressed envelope, to the Radio Society of Great Britain for a full list of names, addresses and contact numbers.

CHAPTER 13

Stand by to transmit

THE great day is here! The post has arrived and you open an official-looking envelope and take out your very own amateur radio licence.

Eagerly you check out the callsign that will be yours and only yours. How will that sound in morse? You run the characters through your head. How does it sound when you say it out loud? Great!

So you are ready to transmit. Of course you have been waiting for this moment for weeks and are anxious to put out your very first signal. Your station is ready to go and you settle in front of your rig to try for that all-important first contact.

Switch on. Choose your band and listen around the dial looking for a loud signal. Perhaps it will be a local amateur you have already asked to help on this, your first contact. Or maybe a strong continental station who is just calling for any station to reply.

Ah! There is G3JNB. He will be happy to work a beginner. He has finished calling. Now is the moment – you press down your transmit switch and start your call.

"G3JNB, G3JNB, this is 2E1QQQ calling you. How do you copy?" Back to receive.

"This is G3JNB. Good morning. Thanks for the call. You are 5 and 9 here in Norwich. Delighted to hear you. You must be a new licensee. Welcome to the bands..."

Well done! Now you really are a radio amateur!

Whilst waiting for your licence, you will have started planning your transmitting station to suit the type of operation

A 40m transceiver kit

PHOTO: LAKE ELECTRONICS

A budget-priced HF transceiver

PHOTO: THANET ELECTRONICS

that you chose for your first day on the air. Perhaps your rig will be a simple low-power CW transmitter for, say, 80 metres. It could be that you have built up a neat little kit of parts and it has

already been tried and tested by a more experienced friend. Working with your existing receiver, you will find that you will start by contacting people with strong signals and, as your skill

A portable VHF transceiver for CW, SSB and FM

PHOTO: SOUTH MIDLANDS COMMUNICATIONS

Packet radio using a home computer is becoming very popular. Here the 9th Reading Girl Guides are operating a station under the supervision of Mark, G4PDH PHOTO: G7AQJ

improves, will then get down to the DX, or long-distance, contacts.

Modern amateur radio rigs come as a combined transmitter and receiver. These are known as 'transceivers' and tend to be compact and very easy to operate in spite of the number of controls spread across the front panel. The handbook will spell out the use of every knob and will instruct you how to tune-up and get the best from the set.

By the time you have taken your tests, you will have learned an amazing amount about the technology of transmitters. The magazines and books will have helped and, hopefully, a visit to a local radio amateur's station will have answered many of your questions.

You will know how to measure your frequency. You will probably have replaced that original long-wire aerial with a new design. A home-made aerial tuner to help match your transmitter into

the aerial is tested and ready, and you have been practising your morse code like mad.

Should you be keen on computers and have your own BBC, Amstrad, Commodore or IBM-compatible PC, then you will already have plans to hook up your transceiver to your keyboard and monitor. A computer is the gateway to all sorts of data transmission, such as AMTOR, packet radio and RTTY. In each of these modes, you communicate using a keyboard instead of voice or a morse key. The computer can even help with the reception and transmission of 'slow-scan television'. Your log and station files can be held in memory and all sorts of design work can be accomplished using the right software.

From now on, the outside world will know you by your callsign and the quality of your signal. The great adventure has started.

The end of the beginning

For many thousands of people, the discovery of amateur radio has been the beginning of an entirely new and unique hobby. Who knows where it may lead you in the years to come?

Certainly you will derive much from its pursuit. Also, an amateur's special relationship with electronics is readily accepted by the electronics industry and can be an aid to rapid professional advancement.

For my part, I hope that you have enjoyed reading these pages and that this final note is merely the end of the beginning of your life as a radio amateur.

73, Victor Brand, G3JNB

It's so easy to solder

T O build your own equipment and to make up connecting plugs and sockets, it is essential that you learn how to solder.

Equipped with a miniature electric soldering iron and a supply of the special, multicore solder obtainable from almost any radio supplier, you will soon be soldering as well as the best of them.

Irons come in various sizes and shapes, of which those shown are a few of the most popular.

The secret of success is a hot iron and clean wire and terminals. Before you get down to making your first joints, you will need a few minutes practice. However, be warned! Hot and liquid solder can damage the table top or carpet, so be sure to cover your working area to avoid complaints from the rest of the household.

Keep the hot tip of your iron and the solder away from your skin, as it can cause a painful burn. Wear overalls or something to protect your clothes, and wear safety goggles. If you have long hair, tie it back or wear a cap.

So, plug in your new iron and rest it on a stand of some sort. Wait a few minutes for it to reach working temperature.

To help the metal flow easily, the tip of your iron must be clean. Wipe it on piece of damp sponge which is normally

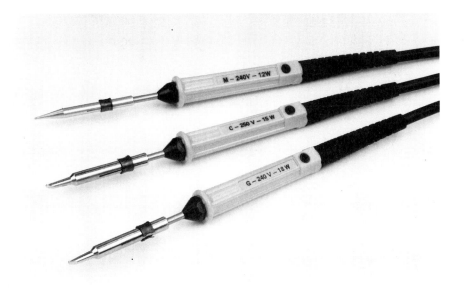

A selection of miniature soldering irons

PHOTO: ANTEX

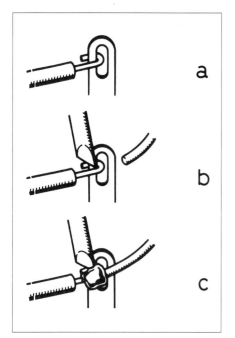

A 25 watt soldering iron and stand. A stand provides a safe place for the iron and may include a sponge pad, as here
PHOTO: ANTEX

How to solder a lead to a tag. (a) Bend the wire round the tag and squeeze it gently with a pair of pliers so it stays put. (b) Heat the wire and tag with the soldering iron, with the solder ready. (c) Quickly apply the solder to the joint, and the metal should flow over both the wire and tag

supplied with the iron's stand. Then just put a dab of solder onto the iron to 'tin' the tip with its own coating of solder.

The wires, tags or terminals that require soldering should be cleaned of all insulation or dirt so that the metal is shining and bright. Copper and brass solder easily but aluminium is really difficult and needs special solder.

To join a copper wire to a solder tag, first connect up the wire to make a sound mechanical joint. You may do this with the aid of a pair of lightweight and pointed pliers.

Now it is time to solder. Wipe the tip of the iron on the sponge, then rest it on the joint, touching a little solder between the two. Within a second or two the

metal should melt and flow easily over the joint. Immediately remove the iron and wait for the soldered joint to cool – you will see the bright silver colour turn slightly duller. Test the joint with a gentle tug, and that is it.

Most joints are quite easy. A few require a little more skill and, in some cases, a heat 'shunt' needs to be clipped onto the component wires to avoid the high temperature damaging delicate parts. A shunt might simply be a pair of forceps, pliers or even a paper clip that will conduct the excess heat away.

To choose your personal soldering iron, select a small bit for fine work and a big one for heavy work. Talk to your more experienced friends and, perhaps, persuade them to let you have a go under their supervision. As with all skills you will find that a little practice makes perfect.

Safety first

ANY activity involving the use of electricity requires the application of basic rules to ensure personal safety at all times.

Obviously, if you are using equipment run from low-voltage batteries there is little danger, except from a risk of fire (or acid) when using car-type batteries – use a fuse close to one terminal of the battery. However, mains-powered radios, transmitters and test equipment must be treated with the same caution and respect that is given to other electrical appliances around the home. The basic rules are:

1. Always use a separate fuse of appropriate rating for each piece of equipment.
2. Be sure that the earth wire in the mains flex is connected to the plug.
3. Don't 'cluster' a whole lot of adapters and plugs into a single wall socket. Instead use a proper multisocket extension board (available from all electrical shops).
4. Earth the metal work of your equipment by joining the connectors from the earth terminals to a heavy wire running to an earth rod or spike outside. Do not link these connections to the earth pin of the mains socket.
5. Outdoor aerials should be shorted to the earth circuit when not in use. This will help to avoid storm damage to your equipment. However, never touch the aerial wire during a thunderstorm - an aerial plugged into a rig is safer than a disconnected one.
6. Unplug the mains lead before you open up any radio cabinet to work inside. If the set has been switched on earlier, do not touch any part of the circuit with your fingers because it could be still holding a high-voltage charge ready to give you a nasty jolt.
7. Never leave a hot soldering iron lying about or an exposed piece of equipment with the power connected.
8. Above all else, if in doubt – DON'T TOUCH.

Finally, if you are fortunate enough to have a whole radio room or area to yourself and can arrange the electrical wiring to suit your station, I recommend that all of your equipment should be in an independent circuit controlled by a master switch by the door. Not only is it most convenient to be able to flip the whole station on or off as you enter or leave the room but, as an added safety factor, any member of the household can switch the power off in the event of an emergency. The use of an 'earth leakage' trip type of protection is also recommended, rather than fuses. A qualified electrician can advise.

All of these rules are common sense and really apply to any hobby or work involving electricity. So cultivate a healthy regard for those volts and always put safety first.

A multi-socket four-way extension board   PHOTO: CIRKIT

Read all about it

F ORTUNATELY for us all, there are a number of excellent magazines and a host of books published for the amateur radio enthusiast. The magazines publish construction articles, news of the exploits of other amateurs and just what to listen for on the bands. The advertising columns are eagerly read for bargains and information on the latest equipment. You will find that you can learn everything about anything by looking into the right book. Indeed, by careful management of your birthday and Christmas present lists, you will soon build up a small library of books that will prove invaluable throughout the years ahead. Clearly, a complete list of titles would not fit into this chapter, so here are just a few to get you started.

Magazines

Radio Communication
The leading radio amateurs' magazine, published monthly by the Radio Society of Great Britain. Mailed to all the members of the Society in over 150 countries and packed with news and technical articles at all levels. Contact the RSGB, Lambda House, Cranborne Road, Potters Bar, Herts EN6 3JE (tel: 0707 59015).

DIY Radio
An entirely new magazine that appeared in pilot form in 1988, again published by the RSGB. Intended for the beginner of any age. Contact the RSGB.

Practical Wireless
Available from newsagents or by subscription, this magazine publishes practical construction articles and radio

news every month. Contact PW Publishing, Enefco House, The Quay, Poole, Dorset BH15 1PP.

Ham Radio Today
Also available monthly from the newsagents and by subscription, an amateur radio magazine with news, reviews and construction features. Contact Argus Specialist Publications Ltd, Argus House, Boundary Way, Hemel Hempstead, Herts HP2 7ST.

Short Wave Magazine
The short-wave listener's own monthly. Available from newsagents and by subscription, with short-wave news for listeners operating on the amateur and

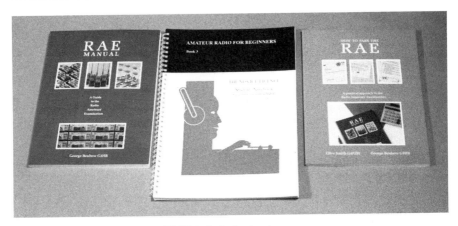

Three books published by the RSGB to help the beginner

broadcast bands, plus the air bands. Contact PW Publishing, Enefco House, The Quay, Poole, Dorset BH15 1PP.

SPRAT
An informal magazine devoted to the activities of the low-power enthusiasts and available quarterly to all members of the G-QRP Society, packed with practical hints and tips and easy-to-build circuits. Contact the G-QRP Society, c/o Rev George Dobbs, G3RJV, St Aidan's Vicarage, 498 Manchester Road, Rochdale, Lancs OL11 3HE.

Monitor
Another informal but excellent magazine enjoyed by the members of the International Short Wave League. Contact the Secretary, 10 Clyde Crescent, Wharton, Winsford, Cheshire CW7 3LA.

QST
The leading American monthly published by the American Radio Relay League and available on subscription via the RSGB or direct. Enjoys a worldwide readership.

Books from the RSGB
The RSGB publishes a large range of books on amateur radio, including:

Morse Code for the Radio Amateur
Teaches you how to learn, send and receive the code.

Radio Amateurs' Examination Manual
The study manual for the full amateur licence.

How to Pass the Radio Amateurs' Examination
A guide to passing the tests with examples of multiple-choice questions.

Amateur Radio Call Book
Packed with useful information, plus a complete listing of all UK and Irish Republic callsigns and addresses.

Practical Wire Antennas
A guide to the design and construction of low-cost wire aerials.

Radio Communication Handbook
The complete text book for the amateur radio student and operator.

Amateur Radio for Beginners
The RSGB is preparing a whole series of books for beginners, of which this is one of the first. Already published is the *Student's Notebook* which is the study guide for the Novice Examination.

Books from *Practical Wireless*

Passport to Amateur Radio
An aid to your studies for an amateur licence and full of useful articles.

Practical Ideas for Radio Amateurs
Hints, tips and practical advice for all transmitting amateurs and short-wave listeners.

Introduction to QRP
Collected articles from *Practical Wireless* published as an introduction to low-power transmitting.

Useful Catalogues

The Maplin Buyers Guide to Electronic Components
Available from W H Smith & Son and from Maplin shops. A huge catalogue of components, kits and electronic equipment, all available on mail order. Published annually. Contact Maplin Electronic Supplies Ltd, PO Box 3, Rayleigh, Essex SS6 8LR (tel: 0702 552911).

Cirkit Electronic Constructors' Catalogue
A comprehensive catalogue of components, kits and electronic equipment. Published regularly and available by post and from leading newsagents. Contact Cirkit Distributors Ltd, Park Lane, Broxbourne, Hertfordshire EN10 7NQ (tel: 0992 444111).

Tandy Electronics Catalogue
A catalogue of electronic equipment and components that are available at over 400 Tandy shops and from Tandy agents nationwide. Obtainable from the shops or by mail from The Tandy Centre, Leamore Lane, Walsall, West Midlands WS2 7PS (tel: 0922 710000).

Marco Trading
A mail-order catalogue of electronic components, test equipment and kits.

Write to Marco Trading, The Maltings, High Street, Wem, Shrewsbury SY4 5EN (tel 0939 32763).

Kit suppliers

Badger Boards, 1180 Aldridge Road, Great Barr, Birmingham B44 8PE (tel: 021-366 6047).

Cambridge Kits, 45 Old School Lane, Milton, Cambridge CB4 6BS.

C M Howes Communications, Eydon, Daventry, Northants NN11 6PT (tel: 0327 60178).

Jandek, 6 Fellows Avenue, Kingswinford, West Midlands DY6 9ET (tel: 0384 288900).

Kanga Products, 3 Limes Road, Folkestone, Kent CT19 4AU (tel: 0303 276171).

Lake Electronics, 7 Middleton Close, Nuthall, Nottingham NG16 1BX.

Index

Introducing

The Radio Society of Great Britain

The Radio Society of Great Britain has a membership of over 35,000 radio amateurs and local radio clubs. The Society represents the interests of amateur radio in the United Kingdom and deals extensively with international and national governing bodies with respect to licensing, frequency allocation and the maintenance of amateur services.

In 1989 the Society launched an initiative to encourage interest in the hobby. Entitled 'Project YEAR' (Youth into Electronics via Amateur Radio), the programme has been developed to include a short training course for all age groups, to teach the basics of the hobby to all those who are keen to learn more about amateur radio and electronics.

The course is of a very simple and practical nature, and may be easily understood by anyone without previous knowledge. Attendance at, and completion of, the course enables the student to sit for an elementary multiple-choice exam (held regularly by the City & Guilds) for those wishing to take out a novice amateur transmitting licence.

Membership of the Society is open to all licensed radio amateurs and short-wave listeners. The Society hopes to have a special category for Novice Licence trainees and licence holders.

INFORMATION PACK You are invited to return the enquiry slip overleaf for our information pack.

Membership services

The Society provides a wide range of services to support the amateur radio movement, of which the following are among the most relevant to new members.

■ DIY RADIO
A regular news sheet, designed to assist the newcomer with the hobby, which is sent to all Novice members.

■ RADIO COMMUNICATION
The leading British radio amateurs' magazine, it is published monthly by the Society and circulated to all full members. The magazine is packed with technical articles and the latest news.

■ QSL BUREAU
This service handles the distribution of QSL cards on a worldwide basis.

■ BOOKS
The Society publishes a wide range of books on amateur radio at reasonable prices. In addition, members enjoy a 15% discount on all titles.

■ EXHIBITIONS
A national exhibition and a number of rallies are organised annually by the Society and the affiliated clubs.

■ NEWS BULLETINS
The latest news is transmitted on amateur bands by GB2RS, the Society's own news broadcasting service.

■ MORSE TESTS
Morse tests for both Novice licensees (at five words per minute) and full licence applications (at 12 words per minute) are held regularly by Society officers.

PLEASE SEND THE

INFORMATION PACK

ON AMATEUR RADIO AND THE RADIO SOCIETY OF GREAT BRITAIN TO:

Name ....

Address ....

....

.... **Post code** ....

I am under 18 years old ❑
I am over 18 years old ❑
(Please tick appropriate box)

My nearest city or large town is ....

Post to:

**THE RADIO SOCIETY OF GREAT BRITAIN
MEMBERSHIP SERVICES DEPARTMENT
LAMBDA HOUSE
CRANBORNE ROAD
POTTERS BAR
HERTS   EN6 3JE**

You've read the book... now see the video!

The Radio Society of Great Britain presents...

AMATEUR RADIO FOR BEGINNERS

Sponsored by: YORKSHIRE TELEVISION ICOM

Catch up with this fascinating video at your local radio club! It consists of two films of 20 minutes each, introducing the hobby and dealing with the practical aspects of getting a transmitting licence.